To us —— to commemorate
our visit to the Lear Exhibition
as "Friends" of the R.A.

Happy Anniversary for the
22nd Time.

1985.

EDWARD LEAR

Bosh and Nonsense

ALLEN LANE

ALLEN LANE
PENGUIN BOOKS LTD
536 KING'S ROAD
LONDON SW10 0UH

FIRST PUBLISHED 1982

ISBN 0 7139 1481 5

SET IN MONOTYPE FOURNIER BY
FOREMOST TYPESETTING LTD, LONDON
PRINTED IN GREAT BRITAIN BY
WILLIAM CLOWES (BECCLES) LTD, BECCLES AND LONDON

FOREWORD

In 1981 two sketchbooks bound in leather and watered silk were found amongst the family papers in Naughton House, Fife. They contain seventy-nine numbered illustrated nonsense limericks in Edward Lear's inimitable style and were composed and drawn in Nice in late 1864 and early 1865 for eleven-year-old Ada Duncan. Catherine Henrietta Adamina Morison Duncan of Naughton was a direct descendant of Admiral Viscount Duncan, victor of the naval battle of Camperdown, and spent a considerable part of her childhood on extensive tours abroad with her peripatetic mama. Ada and her mother must have charmed Lear when they met in Nice. From 61 Promenade des Anglais he wrote them both non-sense letters illustrated with witty self-portraits:

Tuesday 3 January 1865

Dear Miss Duncan,

    I disclose the photograph which I hope you will approve of.

    I got home very safely last night, and partly this was owing to the care taken of me by two remarkably large and amiable Frogs, whose arms I took, and who saw me down the lane. (You will see a true representation of the fact overleaf.) Nothing could exceed the genteel and intelligent expression of their count-enances, except the urbanity of their deport-ment and the melancholy and oblivious sweetness of their voices. They informed me that they were the parents of nine and forty tadpoles of various ages and talents some of whom were expecting shortly to emigrate to Malvern and Mesopotamia.

        Believe me,
        Yours sincerely

Edward Lear.

7 January 1865

My Dear Lady Duncan,

You and Miss Duncan will be much pleased to hear what occurred just after you left yesterday, and I am very sorry you had not happened to stay longer. Imagine how much surprised and gratified I was by a visit from the two considerate Frogs, who brought their two Eldest Tadpoles also to see me. On the other page you will see a correct drawing of the interview. Both of these amiable persons seem much pleased with my 2 lamps, which I regret I did not show you, and one of them was so good as to say that if he were able he would have tried to carry one of the lamps as far as Maison Carabucel to let you see it. They did not stay above 20 minutes, as they had a good way to go home, and I was vexed that there was nothing but a piece of cold lamb in the house and some Marsala, both of which they declined, saying that either watercresses or small beetles would have been pleasant, but that they were not hungry. I did not quite know at points how to be civil to the Tadpoles, as I found that owing to their long tails they could not sit on chairs as their parents did: I therefore put them into a wash hand basin, and they seemed happy enough.

Such kind attentions from foreign persons quite of a different race, and I may [. . . . . . .] from our own, are certainly most delightful: and none the less so for being so unexpected. The Frogs were as good as to add that had I had any oil paintings they would have been

glad to purchase one – but that the damp of
their abode would quite efface watercolour
art.*

> Believe me,
> Yours sincerely
>
> Edward Lear.

*This might well be a wry aside aimed at the constant
stream of visitors to his studio who came to stare but not to
buy. Holbrook Jackson, in his introduction to *The Complete
Nonsense of Edward Lear* (Faber and Faber, 1947), tells how
'At Malta he was dubbed a mystery and a savage' because he
fled from the crowd of visitors who would have thronged

his rooms without dreaming of spending £5 on a drawing.
In a whole season he 'only got £50 from the rich Cannes
public'. He had a bad winter in 1878 at San Remo, having
sold but one drawing for £7, and would have 'come to
grief' had it not been for two friends who bought some of
his smaller oil paintings.

Lear was sixty-two when these letters were written and was engaged in painting topographical scenes at a prodigious rate. A 'Wandering Painter' he described himself, and a 'very energetic and frisky old cove'. The prototypes of Ada's nonsense limericks were written thirty years before for the children at Knowsley Hall, Lord Derby's country house near Liverpool. Some of these were illustrated and added to for publication in 1846 of A *Book of Nonsense*. In 1861 an extended third edition was published. Many of the verses and illustrations written and drawn for Ada are entirely new and unknown, some have similarities to known works and some are variants.

Lear died in 1888 at San Remo on the Italian Riviera; Ada died in 1932.

Photograph of Ada *and her mother*

*The following seventy-nine drawings
are reproduced here
in the same size as the sketchbook originals.*

LIMERICKS AND DRAWINGS

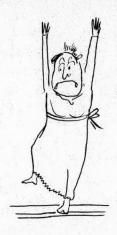

There was an old Lady whose folly, Induced her to sit in a holly:
Wherefrom by a thorn, Her gown being torn, She quickly became melancholly.

There was an old lady whose folly, Induced her to sit in a holly:
Wherefrom by a thorn, her gown being torn, She quickly become melancholly.

1

There was a young Lady of Norway, who casually sat in a doorway.
When the door squeezed her flat — she exclaimed — "What of that?" —
— That courageous young lady of Norway! —

There was a young Lady of Norway, who casually sat in a doorway.
When the door squeezed her flat – she exclaimed "What of that?" – That courageous young lady of Norway!

There was an old person of Rhodes, who strongly objected to Toads.
So he paid some old Cousins to kill them by dozens — That fearful old person of Rhodes.

There was an old Man of the Nile, who sharpened his nails with a file.
When he cut off his thumbs, - he said calmly ___ "This comes ___ of sharpening one's nails with a File!

There was an old man of the Nile, who sharpened his nails with a file.
When he cut off his thumbs – he said calmly – "This comes – of sharpening one's nails with a File!"

There was an old man of the North, who fell into a basin of broth –
But a laudable Cook, twitched him out with a hook – Which saved that old man of the North.

*There was a young Person whose nose, was so long that it reached to her toes —
So she hired an old Lady whose conduct was steady, t carry her wonderful nose.*

6

There was a young Person whose nose, was so long that it reached to her toes –
So she hired an old Lady whose conduct was steady, to carry her wonderful nose.

There was an old man of Jamaica – Who suddenly married a Quaker –
But she cried out – "O lack! I have married a Black!" – Which confused that old man of Jamaica!

There was an old man who said "Hush! – I perceive a small bird in this Bush!" –
When they said – "does it sing?" – He replied – "No such thing! – It's a'building a nest in this bush!"

There was an old Man on some rocks – Who shut up his wife in a box –
When she cried – "let me go!" – He merely said – "No!
Don't make such a noise in that box!"

There was an old man on some rocks – Who shut up his wife in a box –
When she cried – "let me go!" – He merely said – "No! – Don't make such a noise in that box!"

There was an old man of the West – Who wore a pale plum coloured vest;
When they said – Does it fit? – he replied – "Not a bit!" – That uneasy old man of the West.

There was an old man of the Wrekin – whose shoes made a horrible Creaking.
So they said – "Tell us <u>whether</u>, your shoes are of <u>leather</u> or of <u>what</u>, you old man of the <u>Wrekin</u>?"

There was an old man of Peru
Who never knew what he should do,
So he sat on a chair –
And behaved like a bear –
That unhappy old man of Peru. –

There was an old man of Peru Who never knew what he should do,
So he sat on a chair – And behaved like a bear – That unhappy old man of Peru.

12

There was an old person of Burton – Whose answers were rather uncertain;
– When they said – "How d'ye do?" He replied – "Who are you?" – That uncivil old person of Burton.

There was a young lady of Sweden – Eoh went by th slow train to Weedon –
When thy cried "Weedon station!" – She made no observation –
But thought she should go back to Sweden.

There was a young lady of Sweden – Who went by the slow train to Weedon –
When they cried – "Weedon Station!" – She made no observation – But <u>thought</u> she should go back to Sweden.

There was a young Lady of Hull – Who was chased by a virulent Bull.
But she caught up a Spade – and called out – "Who's afraid?" – That remarkable Lady of Hull.

There was an old man who said – "How – shall I flee from this horrible cow? –
I will sit on this stile, and endeavour to smile – Which may soften the heart of that cow!"

There was an old Man of Dundee –
Who frequented the top of a tree –
When disturbed by th Crows –
He abruptly arose –
And said – "I'll return to Dundee."

There was an old man of Dundee – Who frequented the top of a tree –
When disturbed by the Crows – He abruptly arose – And said – "I'll return to Dundee."

There was an old person whose legs – bore a striking resemblence to pegs.
When they said – "Can you toddle?" – He answered – "I waddle –
What else should I do with my legs?"

There was an old person whose legs – bore a striking resemblence to pegs.
When they said – "Can you toddle?" – He answered – "I waddle – What else <u>should</u> I do with my legs?"

There was a young lady of Dorking
Who bought a larger bonnet for walking. –
But its' color & size
So bedazzled her eyes –
That she very soon went back to Dorking.

There was a young Lady of Dorking Who bought a large bonnet for walking –
But its color & size So bedazzled her eyes – That she very soon went back to Dorking.

There was an oldman of the West, Who never could get any rest; — So they set him to spin, on his nose & his chin, which cured that old man of the West.

There was an old man of the West, Who never could get any rest; –
So they set him to spin, on his nose and his chin, which cured that old man of the West.

There was an old man on the coast, Who placidly sate on a post;
When the weather grew cold, he relinquished his hold, And called for some hot buttered toast.

There was an old man on the coast, Who placidly sate on a post;
When the weather grew cold, he relinquished his hold, And called for some hot buttered toast.

There was an old man whose delight, was to play on the trumpet all night – When they said – "You're a bore!" – He answered – "What for? – Mayn't I play on the trumpet all night?"

There was an old man whose delight, was to play on the trumpet all night –
When they said – "You're a bore!" – He answered – "What for? – <u>Mayn't</u> I play on the trumpet all night?"

There was an old person of Troy, whose drink was warm Brandy and Soy;
Which he took with a Spoon, by the light of the Moon – In sight of the City of Troy.

There was an old person of Tartary, who divided his jugular artery -
But he screeched to his wife - And she said - "O! my life! Your loss will be felt by all Tartary!"

There was an old person of Rheims – Who was troubled with horrible dreams –
So to keep him awake – they fed him with Cake – That afflicted old person of Rheims!

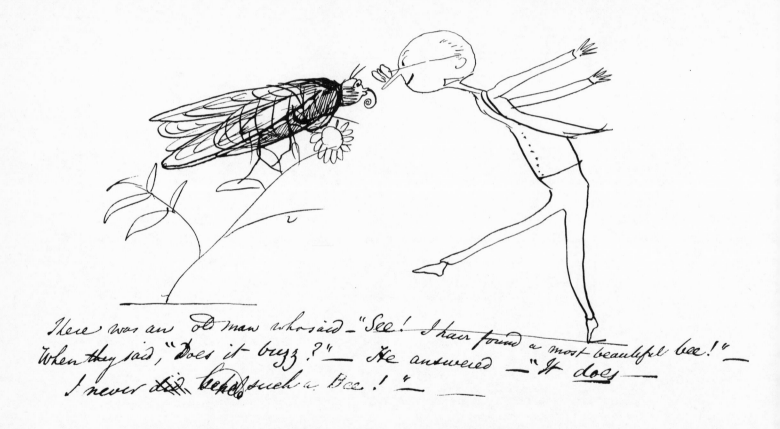

There was an old man who said – "See! I have found a most beautiful bee!" –
When they said, "Does it buzz?" – He answered – "It <u>does</u> – I never beheld such a bee!"

There was a young Lady whose Eyes, were unique as to color & size: —
When she opened them wide — people all turned aside, and started away in surprize.

There was a young Lady whose Eyes, were unique as to color & size: –
When she opened them wide – people all turned aside, and started away in surprize.

There was a young lady of Parma — whose conduct grew calmer & calmer: —
When they said — "Are you dumb?" — She merely said — "Hum!" —
That unpleasant young lady of Parma! —

There was a young lady of Parma – whose conduct grew calmer & calmer: –
When they said – "Are you dumb?" – She merely said – "Hum!" – That unpleasant young lady of Parma!

There was a young Lady of Smyrna, Whose grandmother threatened to burn her:
But she seized on the Cat, & said – "Granny – burn <u>that</u> –! People don't burn young ladies in Smyrna!"

There was an old man of Apulia, whose conduct was rather peculiar:
He fed 15 sons, upon nothing but buns, that corrosive old man of Apulia.

There was an old Lady of Prague – whose answers were horribly vague –:
When they said – "Are these caps?" – She answered – "Per-haps" – That ambiguous old creature of Prague.

There was an old man of the Cape, who possessed a large Barbary Ape —
But the Ape one dark night set the house all alight — Which burned that old man
of the Cape. —

There was an old man of the Cape, who possessed a large Barbary Ape –
But the Ape one dark night set the house all alight – Which burned that old man of the Cape.

There was an old person of Dover, who ran through a field of blue clover —
But some very large bees — stung his nose & his knees — So he suddenly went back to Dover.

There was an old person of Dover, who ran through a field of blue clover –
But some very large bees – stung his nose & his knees – So he suddenly went back to Dover.

33

There was an old person of Dover, who ran through a field of blue clover —
But some very large bees — stung his nose & his knees — So he suddenly went back to Dover.

33

There was an old person of Cadiz – Who was very polite to all ladies –
But in handing his daughter, he fell in the water – Which drowned that old person of Cadiz.

There was a young Lady of Poole – Whose soup was excessively cool –
So she set it to boil – by the aid of some oil – That ingenious young lady of Poole.

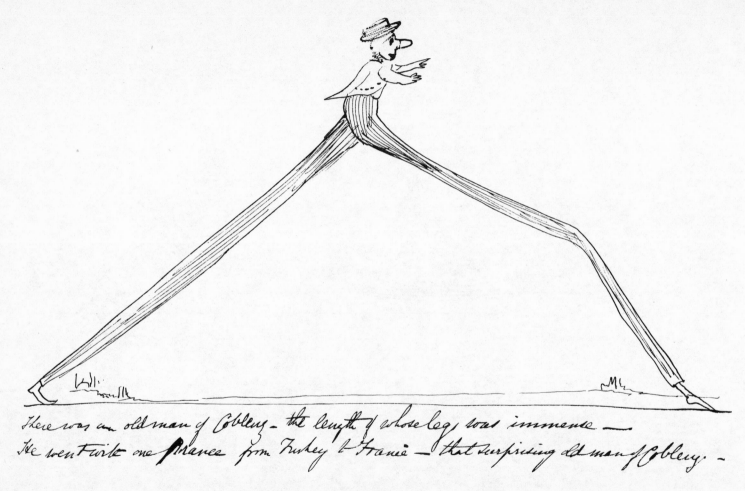

There was an old man of Coblenz — the length of whose legs was immense —
He went with one prance from Turkey to France — that surprising old man of Coblenz.

There was a young lady of Russia – who screamed so that no one could hush her: –
Her screams were extreme: – No one heard such a scream – As was screamed by that Lady of Russia!

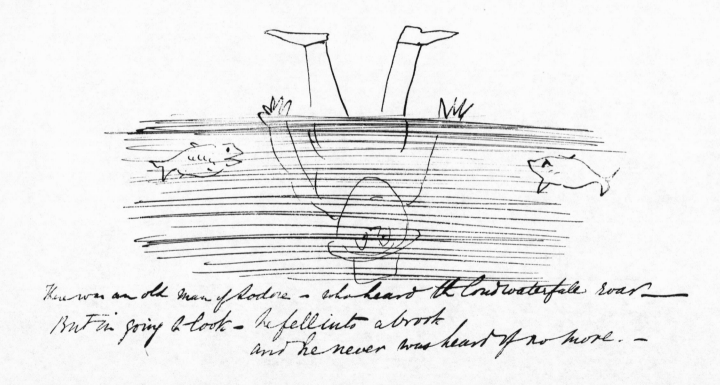

There was an old man of Lodore – who heard th loud waterfall roar –
But in going to look – he fell into a brook
and he never was heard of no more. –

There was an old man of Lodore – who heard the loud waterfall roar –
But in going to look – he fell into a brook and he never was heard of no more.

There was an old man of Leghorn – the smallest that ever was born –
But quickly snapped up he – was once by a puppy – Which finished that man of Leghorn.

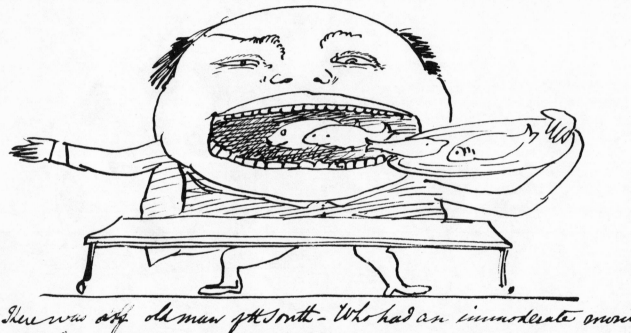

There was an old man of the South – Who had an immoderate mouth.
But in swallowing a dish which was quite full of fish He was choked – that old man of the South.

There was an old man of the east, who gave all his Children a feast.
But their conduct was such – & they all ate so much, that it killed that old man of the East.

There was an old Man of Columbia, who was thirsty & called out for some beer; But they brought it him hot, in a small copper pot – which disgusted that man of Columbia.

There was an old man of Columbia, who was thirsty & called out for <u>some</u> beer;
But they brought it him hot, in a small copper pot – which disgusted that man of Columbia.

There was an old Man of Kilkenny, who never had more than a penny.
And he laid out that money in Onions and Honey, which pleased that old man of Kilkenny.

There was an old Man of Kilkenny, who never had more than a penny.
And he laid out that money in Onions and Honey, which pleased that old man of Kilkenny.

43

There was an old person so silly – He poked his head into a Lily –
But six bees who lived there – filled him full of despair
For they stung that old person so silly.

There was an old person so silly – He poked his head into a Lily –
But six bees who lived there – filled him full of despair For they stung that old person so silly.

*There was an old sailor of Compton, Whose vessel a rock it once bump'd on —
The shock was so great that it damaged the pate of that funny old sailor of Compton.*

There was an old sailor of Compton, whose vessel a rock it once bump'd on –
The shock was so great that it damaged the pate of that funny old sailor of Compton.

45

There was a young Lady of Bute – Who played on a silver=gilt flute –
She played several jigs to her uncle's white pigs, – That melodious young lady of Bute.

There was a young Lady of Bute – Who played on a silver-gilt flute –
She played several jigs to her uncle's white pigs, – That melodious young lady of Bute.

There was a young Lady of Portugal, whose tastes were exceedingly nautical:
She felt deep emotion, on viewing the Ocean, & sighed to be gone out of Portugal.

There was an old person of Sparta, who had 21 sons & one darter —
He weighed them in scales, & fed them with snails, — that oppressive old person of Sparta.

There was an old person of Sparta, who had **21** sons & one darter –
He weighed them in scales, & fed them with snails, – that oppressive old person of Sparta.

There was an old man of Marseilles, whose daughters wore bottle green veils –
They caught some large fish – Which they put in a dish – Which they sent to their pa at Marseilles.

There was an old man of Kamsckatka, who possed a remarkably <u>fat</u> cur; –
His gait & his waddle, were held as a model, – to all the young dogs of Khamskatka.

There was a young lady of Turkey — who wept when the weather was murky:
When the weather grew fine — she ceased to repine — that capricious young lady of Turkey.

*There was an old man whose repose, Consisted in warming his toes : –
When they said – "Are they done?" – He answered " What fun! –
Do you think I'm a cooking my toes?"*

There was an old man whose repose, Consisted in warming his toes: –
When they said – "Are they done?" – He answered "What fun! – Do you think I'm a'cooking my toes?"

There was an old man whose despair induced him to purchase a bear
He played on some trumpets & fed upon crumpets – which rather assuaged his despair.

53

There was an old person of Sidon, who bought a small poney to ride on
But he found him too small to leap over a wall, So he walked – that old person of Sidon.

There was an old Man of Madras, who rode on a creamcoloured ass
But the length of his ears so promoted his fears – that it killed that old Man of Madras.

There was an old person whose mirth, Induced her to leap from the earth –
But in leaping too quick – he exclaimed – I'm too sick
To leap any more from the earth.

There was an old person whose mirth, Induced him to leap from the earth –
But in leaping too quick – he exclaimed – I'm too sick To leap any more from the earth.

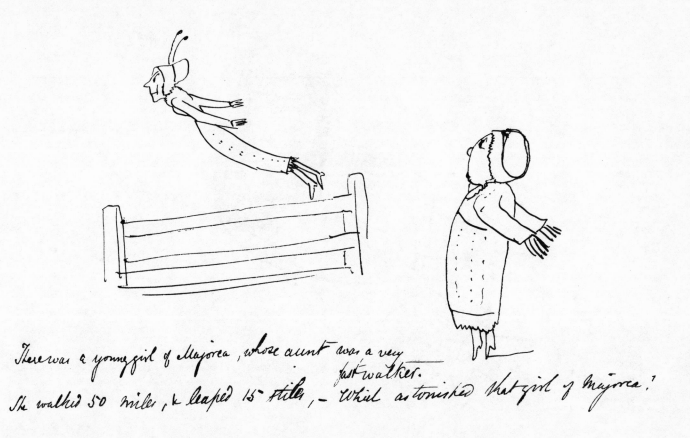

There was a young girl of Majorca, whose aunt was a very fast walker.
She walked 50 miles, & leaped 15 stiles, – Which astonished that girl of Majorca!

There was an old Lady of Leeds, who was always a'doing good deeds –
She sate on some rocks with her feet in a box – & her neck was surrounded with beads.

There was an old man in a boat who complained of a pain in his throat.
When they said – "Can you screech?" He replied – "I beseech You won't make any noise in my boat!"

There was an old man of Vesuvius, who studied the works of Vitruvius.
When the flames burned his book, to drinking he took Which destroyed that old man of Vesuvius.

There was an old man of Vesuvius, who studied the works of Vitruvius.
When the flames burned his book, to drinking he took Which destroyed that old man of Vesuvius.

There was a young Lady of Welling, whose praise all th world was a telling:
She played on the Harp, ~~to played t~~ and caught several Carp, —
That accomplished young Lady of Welling. —

There was a young Lady of Welling, whose praise all the world was a'telling:
She played on the Harp, and caught several Carp, – That accomplished young Lady of Welling.

There was a young person of Wales, who caught a large fish without scales: –
When she cried – "only look – at the end of my hook! – ! –" That lively young person of Wales.

There was an old man of Peru, who never knew what he should do
So he ran up & down till the sun turned him brown —
That uneasy old man of Peru

There was an old man of Peru, who never knew what he should do
So he ran up & down till the sun turned him brown – That uneasy old man of Peru.

There was an old man of New York, who murdered hisself with a fork –:
But nobody cried – tho' he very soon died – That unlucky old man of New York.

There was an old Man of th' Abruzzi – So blind that he couldn't his foot see:
When they said "that's your toe" – he exclaimed – "Is that so?" – That unpleasant old Man of th' Abruzzi.

There was an old person of Ischia, Whose conduct grew friskier & friskier _
He danced several jigs, and fed on green figs
That indigenous person of Ischia.

There was an old person of Ischia, Whose conduct grew friskier & friskier –
He danced several jigs, and fed on green figs That indigenous person of Ischia.

There was an old man of the Isles – Whose face was pervaded with smiles:
He sang highdiddlediddle – & played on the fiddle – That lively old man of the Isles.

There was an old man of Moldavia, who had the most curious behaviour:
For while he was able he slept on a table —
That singular Man of Moldavia. —

There was an old man of Moldavia, who had the most curious behaviour:
For while he was able he slept on a table – That singular Man of Moldavia.

There was an old man of Bohemia, whose daughter was christened Skrokemia:
But one day to his grief, she ran off with a thief – That unhappy old man of Bohemia.

There was an old person of Buda, whose conduct grew ruder and ruder –
Till one day with a hammer they silenced his clamour By smashing that person of Buda.

There was an old man whose desire, Was to sit with his feet in the fire:
When they said – "are they 'ot?" – He replied – "No – they're not! you must put some more coals on the fire."

There was an old man who said – "Well! – This <u>is</u> a remarkable bell!
"I have pulled night & day – till my hair has grown grey – But nobody answers this bell!"

There was an old person of Calais — Who lived in a blue marble palace.
But on coming downstairs, he encountered some bears —
Who swallowed that person of Calais.

There was an old person of Calais – Who lived in a blue marble palace:
But on coming downstairs, he encountered some bears – Who swallowed that person of Calais.

There was an old man at a Casement, who held up his hands in amazement -
When they said - "Sir! you'll fall!!" - He replied - "Not at all" - That astucious old man at a Casement.

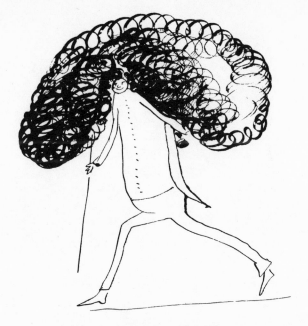

There was an old person of Dutton, whose head was as small as a button
So to make it look big – he purchased a wig – And rapidly rushed about Dutton.

There was an old man with a light, who was dressed in a garment of white: He held a small candle with never a handle, And danced all the merry long night.

There was an old man with a light, who was dressed in a garment of white:
He held a small candle with never a handle, And danced all the merry long night.

There was an old person of Gretna – who rushed down the Crater of Etna
When they cried "is it hot?" – he replied – "No it's not" – That mendacious old person of Gretna.

There was an old man who said "O! — Let us come where the humblebees grow!
There are no less than 5 sitting still on a hive
Singing songs to their children below.

There was an old man who said "O! – Let us come where the humblebees grow!
There are no less than 5 sitting still on a hive Singing songs to their children below.

There was an old man who made bold, To affirm that the weather was cold:
So he ran up & down, in his grandmother's gown —
Which was woollen, & not very old.

There was an old man who made bold, To affirm that the weather was cold:
So he ran up & down, in his grandmother's gown – Which was woollen, & not very old.